Santa's WorkShop

Christmas Sticker and Activity Fun

igloobooks

Odd Elf Out

Christmas is on its way, so the elf boss has called a meeting.
Can you spot which one he is? He's different to all the rest!

Twin Toys

The elves' first job is to sort the toys into piles.
Help them by matching each toy to its pair.

Answers on page 16

A-mazing Elf

Ernie The Elf has been sent to the stockroom to collect some toys. Can you help him find his way through the windy corridors?

Answers on page 16

Conveyor Belt Chase

Santa's napping, so the elves are playing! Join in the fun with your friends to see who can reach the finish first.

You Will Need:

Elf stickers
Four coins
A dice

Find the four elf stickers on your sticker sheet and place them on coins to make counters. Each player takes a turn to roll the dice and move their counter the number rolled. If a player lands on a special instruction square, they must read it aloud and follow the instructions. The first person to reach the finish wins.

Painting Pickle

Oh no, the elves have played too long and there's still a lot of work to do! Use your best pens to help them paint the rest of the toys.

Sleigh Sprint

The elves need to practise running to the sleigh so they're fast enough for Christmas Eve. Count the obstacles to see which elf will be the quickest.

Answers on page 16

Santa's Secret

The toy safe has accidentally been locked shut! Use the stickers on the sticker sheet to solve the safe's pattern code.

Forgotten Finds

The elves are off to bed for a rest, but they've left some things laying around the workshop. Can you match the silhouettes to the lost items?

Answers on page 16

Imp Inspection

After a long winter's sleep, the elves are back at work. Lend a hand with their final checks by pairing the complete toys with the close-ups.

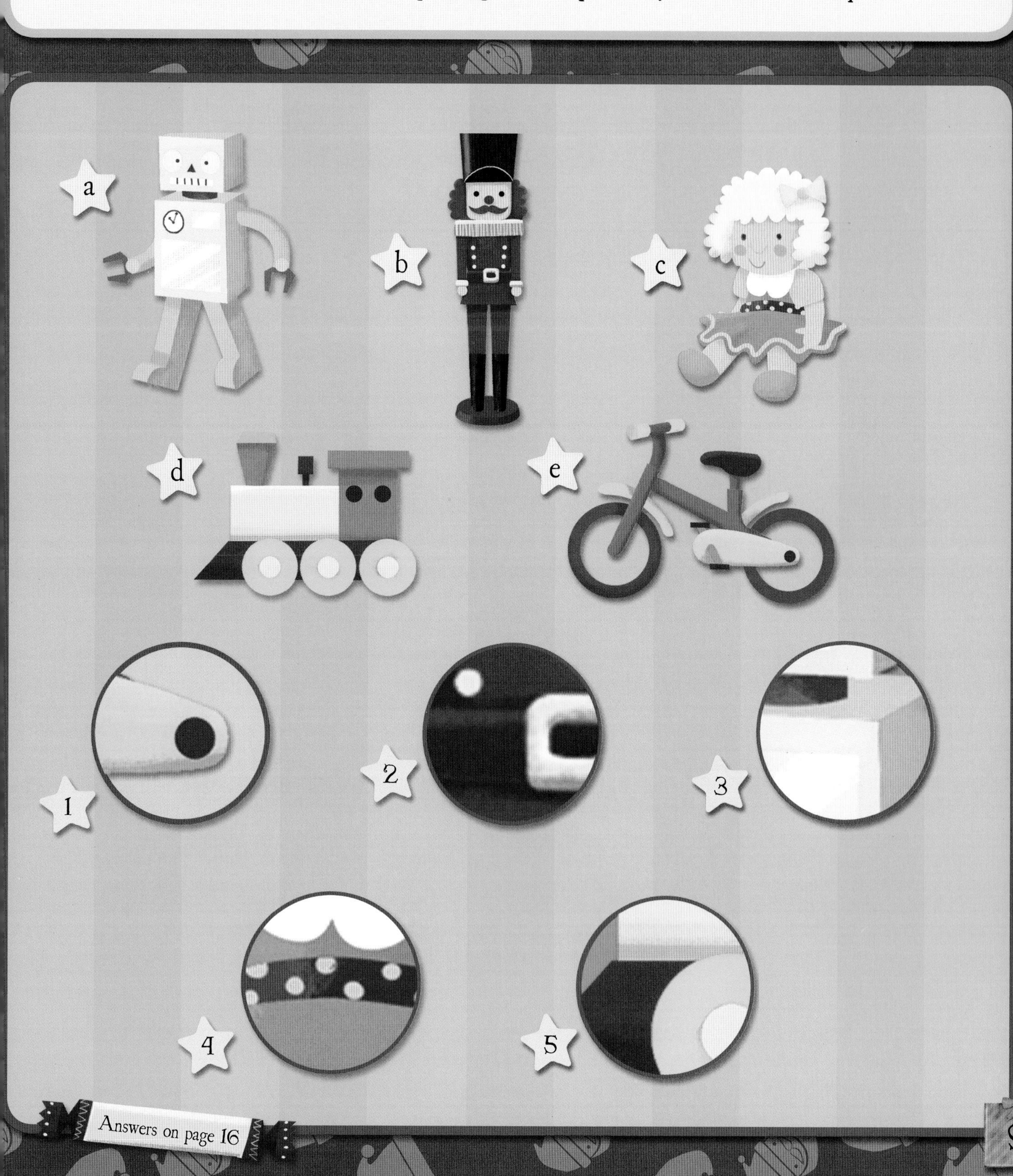

Answers on page 16

Where Is Everyone?

Uh-oh! Santa's lost his glasses. Look at the pictures on the right and see how many of each item you can find in the scene. Can you spot all ten elves?

Answers on page 16

Double Time

It's almost Christmas Eve, so the elves really need to work hard now. Spot the six differences between the two pictures to speed them up.

Answers on page 16

Candy Cane Clues

Santa has asked the elves to pack snacks onto the sleigh, but one of them has been nibbling! Use the clues to find the sweet stealer.

Clues

1. He is wearing green and yellow socks.
2. He has two buttons on his top.
3. He has a bell at the end of his hat.
4. He has red rosy cheeks.

Answers on page 16

Pixie Picture

Sasha The Elf is doodling on her lunch break, but she's got to get back to the workshop again. Can you complete the rest of her drawing instead?

Lost Helper

Ernie The Elf has got lost while loading up the sleigh with presents. Draw a line through all the squares on the grid, without using any diagonal lines, to help him.

Answers on page 16

It's Party Time!

The elves' work is done, so Santa is saying thanks with a big party. Can you spot the pictures below? Which picture doesn't belong here?

Answers on page 16

Answers

Page 2: Odd Elf Out
d is the elf boss

Page 2: Twin Toys
a-5, b-3, c-1, d-2, e-4

Page 3: A-mazing Elf

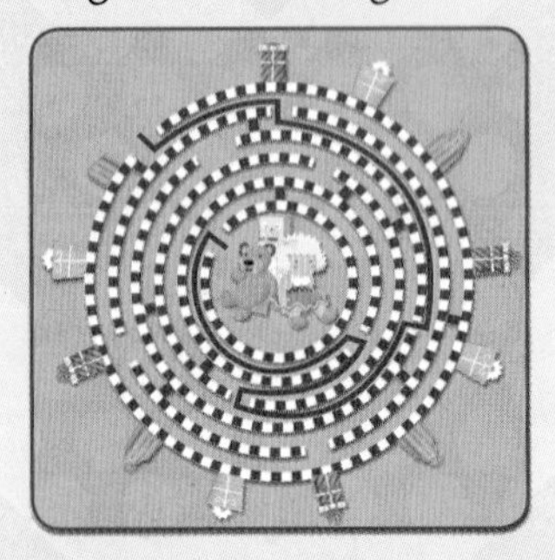

Page 7: Sleigh Sprint
a has the least obstacles in the way

Page 8: Santa's Secret

Page 8: Forgotten Finds
a-3, b-1, c-4, d-2

Page 9: Imp Inspection
a-3, b-2, c-4, d-5, e-1

Pages 10-11: Where Is Everyone?
a = 4, b = 5, c = 3, d = 8

Page 12: Double Time

Page 13: Candy Cane Clues
b is the correct elf

Page 14: Lost Helper

Page 15: It's Party Time!
Picture b isn't in the party scene